Am I Bothered?

JIM DAVIS

RR
RAVETTE PUBLISHING

First published by Ravette Publishing 2007.
Reprinted 2007

Printed and bound in Great Britain
for Ravette Publishing Limited,
Unit 3, Tristar Centre,
Star Road, Partridge Green,
West Sussex RH13 8RA

ISBN: 978-1-84161-286-7

SNIFF
SNIFF
SNIFF
SNIFF

JIM DAVIS 12-22

JIM DAVIS 12-23

ODIE, LET'S TALK EFFORT VERSUS RETURN HERE

YOU KNOW, YOU CAN STILL LEAD A POINTLESS LIFE WITHOUT ALL THAT RUNNING AROUND

JIM DAVIS 2-10

YOU'RE PROBABLY WONDERING WHY THIS PLUNGER IS ON MY FACE

I REFUSE TO PLAY YOUR LITTLE GAME

OTHER GARFIELD BOOKS AVAILABLE

Pocket Books	Price	ISBN
Below Par	£3.50	978-1-84161-152-5
Compute This!	£3.50	978-1-84161-194-5
Don't Ask!	£3.99	978-1-84161-247-8
Feed Me!	£3.99	978-1-84161-242-3
Get Serious	£3.99	978-1-84161-265-2
Gotcha!	£3.50	978-1-84161-226-3
I Am What I Am!	£3.99	978-1-84161-243-0
I Don't Do Perky	£3.50	978-1-84161-195-2
Kowabunga	£3.99	978-1-84161-246-1
Light Of My Life	£3.50	978-1-85304-353-6
Pop Star	£3.50	978-1-84161-151-8
S.W.A.L.K.	£3.50	978-1-84161-225-6
Wan2tlk?	£3.99	978-1-84161-264-5
What's Not to Like? (new)	£3.99	978-1-84161-285-0

new titles available Feb 2008 ...

	Price	ISBN
No. 59 - Time to Delegate	£3.99	978-1-84161-296-6
No. 60 - Numero Uno	£3.99	978-1-84161-297-3

Theme Books	Price	ISBN
Behaving Badly	£4.50	978-1-85304-892-0
Cat Napping	£4.50	978-1-84161-087-0
Creatures Great & Small	£3.99	978-1-85304-998-9
Entertains You	£4.50	978-1-84161-221-8
Healthy Living	£3.99	978-1-85304-972-9
Pigging Out	£4.50	978-1-85304-893-7
Slam Dunk!	£4.50	978-1-84161-222-5
Successful Living	£3.99	978-1-85304-973-6
The Seasons	£3.99	978-1-85304-999-6

2-in-1 Theme Books	Price	ISBN
All In Good Taste	£6.99	978-1-84161-209-6
Easy Does It	£6.99	978-1-84161-191-4
Lazy Daze	£6.99	978-1-84161-208-9
Licensed to Thrill	£6.99	978-1-84161-192-1
Out For The Couch	£6.99	978-1-84161-144-0
The Gruesome Twosome	£6.99	978-1-84161-143-3

Classics	Price	ISBN
Volume One	£6.99	978-1-85304-970-5
Volume Two	£5.99	978-1-85304-971-2
Volume Three	£5.99	978-1-85304-996-5
Volume Four	£6.99	978-1-85304-997-2
Volume Five	£6.99	978-1-84161-022-1
Volume Six	£6.99	978-1-84161-023-8
Volume Seven	£5.99	978-1-84161-088-7
Volume Eight	£5.99	978-1-84161-089-4
Volume Nine	£6.99	978-1-84161-149-5
Volume Ten	£6.99	978-1-84161-150-1

Classics (cont'd ...)	Price	ISBN
Volume Eleven	£6.99	978-1-84161-175-4
Volume Twelve	£6.99	978-1-84161-176-1
Volume Thirteen	£6.99	978-1-84161-206-5
Volume Fourteen	£6.99	978-1-84161-207-2
Volume Fifteen	£5.99	978-1-84161-232-4
Volume Sixteen	£5.99	978-1-84161-233-1
Volume Seventeen	£6.99	978-1-84161-250-8
Volume Eighteen	£6.99	978-1-84161 251-5
Gift Books (new series)		
Don't Know, Don't Care	£4.99	978-1-84161-279-9
Get a Grip	£4.99	978-1-84161-282-9
I Don't Do Ordinary	£4.99	978-1-84161-281-2
Keep your Attitude, I have my own	£4.99	978-1-84161-278-2
Little Books		
C-c-c-caffeine	£2.50	978-1-84161-183-9
Food 'n' Fitness	£2.50	978-1-84161-145-7
Laughs	£2.50	978-1-84161-146-4
Love 'n' Stuff	£2.50	978-1-84161-147-1
Surf 'n' Sun	£2.50	978-1-84161-186-0
The Office	£2.50	978-1-84161-184-6
Zzzzzz	£2.50	978-1-84161-185-3
Miscellaneous		
Colour Collection Book 1 (new)	£10.99	978-1-84161-293-5
Treasury 7	£10.99	978-1-84161-248-5
Treasury 6	£10.99	978-1-84161-229-4
Treasury 5	£10.99	978-1-84161-198-3
Treasury 4	£10.99	978-1-84161-180-8
Treasury 3	£9.99	978-1-84161-142-6

All Garfield books are available at your local bookshop or from the publisher at the address below.

Just send your order with your payment and name and address details to:-

Ravette Publishing, Unit 3, Tristar Centre, Star Road, Partridge Green, West Sussex RH13 8RA
(tel: 01403 711443 ... email: ravettepub@aol.com)

Prices and availability are subject to change without notice.

Please enclose a cheque or postal order made payable to **Ravette Publishing** to the value of the cover price of the book/s and allow the following for UK postage and packing:-

70p for the first book + 40p for each additional book
except Garfield Treasuries & Colour Collection... when please add £3.00 per copy for p&p.